CW00402986

STATUTORY INSTRUMENTS

1996 No. 972

ENVIRONMENTAL PROTECTION

The Special Waste Regulations 1996

Made - - - -	*28th March 1996*
Laid before Parliament	*1st April 1996*
Coming into force	*1st September 1996*

ARRANGEMENT OF REGULATIONS

[DOE 0648]

SCHEDULES

The Secretary of State for the Environment, as respects England, the Secretary of State for Wales, as respects Wales, and the Secretary of State for Scotland, as respects Scotland, being Ministers designated(a) for the purposes of section 2(2) of the European Communities Act 1972(b) in relation to measures relating to the regulation and control of the transit, import and export of waste (including recyclable materials), the prevention, reduction and elimination of pollution caused by waste and the requirement for an assessment of the impact on the environment of projects likely to have significant effects on the environment, in exercise of the powers conferred upon them by section 2(2) of that Act, sections 3(1), 17, 30(4) and (5) and 104(1) of the Control of Pollution Act 1974(c), sections 33(3), 34(5), 62(1) to (3), 74(6), 75(8) and 78 of the Environmental Protection Act 1990(d) (having, in particular, had regard in exercising their powers under section 33(3) of that Act to the matters specified in section 33(4) of that Act) and of all other powers enabling them in that behalf, hereby make the following Regulations:

Citation, commencement, extent, application and interpretation

1.—(1) These Regulations may be cited as the Special Waste Regulations 1996 and shall come into force on 1st September 1996.

(2) These Regulations do not extend to Northern Ireland.

(3) These Regulations do not apply in relation to any special waste in respect of which, in accordance with regulation 26 below, the Control of Pollution (Special Waste) Regulations 1980(e) continue to have effect.

(4) In these Regulations, unless the context otherwise requires—

"the 1990 Act" means the Environmental Protection Act 1990;

"the 1994 Regulations" means the Waste Management Licensing Regulations 1994(f);

"Agency" means

(a) in relation to places, premises and sites in England and Wales, the Environment Agency established by section 1 of the Environment Act 1995(g); and

---

(a) S.I. 1993/2661, 1992/2870 and 1988/785.

(b) 1972 c.68.

(c) 1974 c.40; section 3(1) is repealed, and section 17 is prospectively repealed, by Part II of Schedule 16 to the Environmental Protection Act 1990 (c.43); the repeal of section 3(1) came into force on 1st May 1994 (save for certain purposes, in respect of which other dates are appointed) by virtue of S.I. 1994/1096 (as amended by S.I. 1994/2487 and 1994/3234).

(d) 1990 c.43; section 62 is amended by paragraph 80 of Schedule 22 to the Environment Act 1995 (c.25) and section 78 is amended by paragraph 7 of Schedule 4 to the Radioactive Substances Act 1993 (c.12).

(e) S.I. 1980/1709, amended by S.I. 1988/1562, 1988/1790 and 1994/1137 and by Part IV of Schedule 6 to the Radioactive Substances Act 1993 (c.12).

(f) S.I. 1994/1056, amended by S.I. 1995/288, 1995/1950, 1996/634.

(g) 1995 c.25.

(b) in relation to places, premises and sites in Scotland, the Scottish Environment Protection Agency established by section 20 of that Act;

"the approved classification and labelling guide" means the document entitled "Approved guide to the classification and labelling of substances and preparations dangerous for supply (Second edition)"(a) approved by the Health and Safety Commission on 18th October 1994 for the purposes of the Chemicals (Hazard Information and Packaging for Supply) Regulations 1994(b);

"the approved supply list" means the document entitled "Approved Supply List (2nd Edition)—Information approved for the classification and labelling of substances and preparations dangerous for supply"(c) approved by the Health and Safety Commission on 18th October 1994 for the purposes of the Chemicals (Hazard Information and Packaging for Supply) Regulations 1994;

"carrier", in relation to a consignment of special waste, means the person who collects that waste from the premises at which it is being held and transports it to another place;

"carrier's round" in relation to consignments of special waste, means a journey made by a carrier during which he collects more than one consignment of special waste and transports all consignments collected to the same consignee who is specified in the consignment note;

"carrier's schedule" means a schedule prepared in accordance with regulation 8;

"consignee", in relation to a consignment of special waste, means the person to whom that waste is to be transported;

"consignment note", in relation to a consignment of special waste, means a note in a form corresponding to the form set out in Schedule 1 to these Regulations, or in a form substantially to the like effect, and giving at any time the details required by these Regulations to be shown in respect of that consignment (including, where the consignment is one in a succession of consignments, any details required to be shown in respect of other consignments in the succession);

"consignor", in relation to a consignment of special waste, means the person who causes that waste to be removed from the premises at which it is being held;

"controlled waste" has the same meaning as in Part II of the 1990 Act(d);

"conveyance" includes a vehicle designed to carry goods by road or rail and a vessel designed to carry goods by water;

"harbour area" has the same meaning as in the Dangerous Substances in Harbour Areas Regulations 1987(e);

"the Hazardous Waste Directive" means Council Directive 91/689/EEC on hazardous waste, as amended by Council Directive 94/31/EC(f);

"household waste" has the same meaning as it has for the purposes of subsection (2) of section 33 (prohibition on unauthorised or harmful deposit, treatment or disposal etc. of waste) of the 1990 Act(g);

"premises" includes any ship;

"relevant code", in relation to a consignment note or carrier's schedule, means the code assigned in accordance with regulation 4 to the consignment of special waste to which the consignment note or carrier's schedule relates or, where the consignment is one in a carrier's round, to the consignments in that round;

"risk phrase" means the risk phrase shown under Part III of the approved supply list;

(a) The approved classification and labelling guide is available from HSE Books, PO Box 1999, Sudbury, Suffolk, CO10 6FS.
(b) S.I. 1994/3247.
(c) The approved supply list is available from HSE Books, PO Box 1999, Sudbury, Suffolk, CO10 6FS.
(d) *See* section 75 of the Environmental Protection Act 1990 and the Controlled Waste Regulations 1992 (S.I. 1992/588, amended by S.I. 1993/566, 1994/1056 and 1995/288).
(e) S.I. 1987/37.
(f) Council Directive 91/689/EEC is to be found at OJ No. L 377, 31.12.1991, p.20; Council Directive 94/31/EC at OJ No. L 168, 2.7.1994, p.28. *See also* Council Decision 94/904/EC (OJ No. L 356, 31.12.94, p.14).
(g) *See* section 75(5) and (8) of the Environmental Protection Act 1990, and the Controlled Waste Regulations 1992.

"ship" means a vessel of any type whatsoever operating in the marine environment including submersible craft, floating craft and any structure which is a fixed or floating platform;

"special waste" has the meaning given by regulation 2 of these Regulations; and

"waste management licence" has the meaning given by section 35(1) of the 1990 Act(a).

Meaning of special waste

2.—(1) Subject to paragraphs (5) and (6), any controlled waste

(a) to which a six-digit code is assigned in the list set out in Part I of Schedule 2 to these Regulations (which reproduces the list of hazardous waste annexed to Council Decision 94/904/EC(b) establishing a list of hazardous waste pursuant to Article 1(4) of the Hazardous Waste Directive); and

(b) which, subject to paragraph (3), displays any of the properties specified in Part II of that Schedule (which reproduces Annex III to the Hazardous Waste Directive),

is special waste.

(2) Subject to paragraph (6), any other controlled waste which

(a) displays the property H3A (first indent), or subject to paragraphs (3) and (5), H4, H5, H6, H7 or H8 specified in Part II of Schedule 2, or

(b) is a medicinal product, as defined in section 130 of the Medicines Act 1968(c) (meaning of "medicinal product" etc.), of a description, or falling within a class, specified in an order under section 58 of that Act(d) (medicinal products on prescription only),

is special waste.

(3) For the purposes of paragraphs (1) and (2), waste displays a property mentioned in Part II of Schedule 2 as toxic, very toxic, harmful, corrosive, irritant or carcinogenic, if it is so classified or, being so classified, has a risk phrase assigned to it or is placed in a category by the approved classification and labelling guide, as the case may be—

(i) in the case of a substance which is both listed in the approved supply list and present at or above the concentration limit applicable under Part V of that List, on the basis of that list; or

(ii) in the case of any other substance, on the basis of the criteria laid down in the approved classification and labelling guide.

(4) Except in the case of a substance listed in the approved supply list and present at or above the concentration limit applicable under Part V of that List, the test methods to be used, for the purposes of deciding which (if any) of the properties mentioned in Part II of Schedule 2 to these Regulations are to be assigned to a substance, are those described in Annex V to Council Directive 67/548/EEC, as amended(e).

(5) Controlled waste which, apart from this paragraph, would be special waste is not special waste if it displays any of the properties H4 to H8 below the threshold shown as applicable to that property in Part III of Schedule 2 (which reproduces those thresholds set out in Article 1 of Council Decision 94/904/EC in so far as they are relevant).

(6) Household waste is not special waste.

(a) Section 35 is modified by paragraph 9 of Part I of Schedule 4 to the Waste Management Licensing Regulations 1994.
(b) OJ No. L 356, 31.12.1994, p.14.
(c) 1968 c.67; section 130 is amended by paragraph 3(7) to (10) of Schedule 1, and Schedule 2, to the Animal Health and Welfare Act 1984 (c.40).
(d) Section 58 is amended by section 1 of the Medicinal Products: Prescription by Nurses etc. Act 1992 (c.28).
(e) OJ No. 196, 16.8.1967, p.1 as amended by Commission Directive 92/69/EEC (OJ No. L 383, 29.12.1992, p.1).

Certain radioactive waste to be special waste

3. Section 62 (special provision with respect to certain dangerous and intractable waste) of the 1990 Act(**a**) shall have effect, without modification, so as to empower the Secretary of State to make provision for waste which would be controlled waste but for the fact that it is radioactive waste within the meaning of the Radioactive Substances Act 1993(**b**); and paragraphs (1) and (2) of regulation 2 shall apply to any such waste as if it were controlled waste.

Coding of consignments

4.—(1) An Agency shall assign or supply forthwith to any person, on request, for the purpose of assigning to a consignment of special waste or, where the consignment is one in a carrier's round, to the consignments in that round, a code unique to that consignment or round, as the case may be.

(2) A code assigned or supplied in accordance with paragraph (1) may consist of letters, numbers or symbols, or any combination of letters, numbers and symbols, or a bar code which enables the consignment or carrier's round, as the case may be, to be identified electronically.

Consignment notes: standard procedure

5.—(1) Except in a case to which regulation 6, 8 or 9 applies, this regulation applies where a consignment of special waste is to be removed from the premises at which it is being held.

(2) Before the consignment is removed—

    (a) five copies of the consignment note shall be prepared, and, on each copy, Parts A and B shall be completed and the relevant code entered;

    (b) the consignor shall ensure that one of those copies (on which Parts A and B have been completed and the relevant code entered) is furnished to the Agency for the place to which the consignment is to be transported;

    (c) the carrier shall complete Part C on each of the four remaining copies; and

    (d) the consignor—

        (i) shall complete Part D on each of those copies;

        (ii) shall retain one copy (on which Parts A to D have been completed and the relevant code entered); and

        (iii) shall give the three remaining copies (on which Parts A to D have been completed and the relevant code entered) to the carrier.

(3) The carrier shall ensure that the copies which he has received—

    (a) travel with the consignment; and

    (b) are given to the consignee on delivery of the consignment.

(4) Subject to regulation 10, on receiving the consignment the consignee shall—

    (a) complete Part E on the three copies of the consignment note given to him;

    (b) retain one copy;

    (c) give one copy to the carrier; and

    (d) forthwith furnish one copy to the Agency for the place to which the consignment has been transported.

(5) The carrier shall retain the copy of the consignment note given to him by the consignee.

(**a**) Section 62 is amended by paragraph 80 of Schedule 22 to the Environment Act 1995 (c.25).

(**b**) 1993 c.12. Section 78 of the Environmental Protection Act 1990 (which is amended by paragraph 7 of Schedule 4 to the Radioactive Substances Act 1993) provides that Part II of the 1990 Act does not apply to radioactive waste as defined in the 1993 Act save to the extent that the Secretary of State so provides in regulations.

Consignment notes: cases in which pre-notification is not required

6.—(1) For the purposes of regulation 7, except in a case to which regulation 8 applies, this regulation applies—

    (a) subject to paragraph (2)(a), to the removal, from the premises at which it is being held, of each of the second and any subsequent consignment of special waste in a succession of consignments of special waste,

    (b) subject to paragraph (2)(b), to the removal as a consignment of special waste of a product or material for the purposes of the return by the person to whom the product or material had been supplied to the person who supplied it to him or who manufactured it,

    (c) subject to paragraph (2)(c), to the removal of a consignment of special waste where the consignor and the consignee are bodies corporate belonging to the same group,

    (d) to the removal from a ship in a harbour area of a consignment of special waste to a conveyance for transportation to a place outside that area, and

    (e) to the removal of a consignment of special waste which consists entirely of lead acid motor vehicle batteries.

(2) This regulation does not apply unless—

    (a) in the case mentioned in paragraph (1)(a), in respect of each consignment—

        (i) the waste is of the same description as the waste in the first of the consignments in the succession;

        (ii) the consignor is the same person;

        (iii) the consignee is the same person;

        (iv) the premises from which the consignment is removed are the same;

        (v) the place to which the consignment is transported is the same; and

        (vi) the removal of the consignment takes place within one year of the removal of the first consignment in the succession;

    (b) in the case mentioned in paragraph (1)(b), the person to whom the product or material was supplied is satisfied that, as supplied, the product or material fails to meet any specification which he expected it to meet;

    (c) in the case mentioned in paragraph (1)(c), the removal is for the purposes of an operation within either paragraph 15 of Part III, or paragraph 13 of Part IV, of Schedule 4 to the 1994 Regulations, and the consignee either—

        (i) is the holder of a waste management licence which authorises the relevant operation; or

        (ii) carries on any activity to which section 33(1)(a) and (b) of the 1990 Act(**a**) does not apply by virtue of regulation 16 or 17 of the 1994 Regulations.

(3) In paragraph (1)(c) "group", in relation to a body corporate, means that body corporate, any other body corporate which is its holding company or subsidiary and any other body corporate which is a subsidiary of that holding company; and for these purposes—

"body corporate" does not include a corporation sole or a Scottish partnership, but includes a company incorporated elsewhere than in Great Britain; and

"holding company" and "subsidiary" have the meaning given by section 736 of the Companies Act 1985(**b**).

Consignment notes: procedure where pre-notification is not required

7. Paragraph (2), with the exception of sub-paragraph (b), and paragraphs (3) to (5) of regulation 5 shall apply in cases to which regulation 6 applies as if—

    (a) "four" were substituted for "five" in sub-paragraph (a) of paragraph (2);

(**a**) Section 33(1)(a) and (b) is modified by paragraph 9 of Part I of Schedule 4 to the Waste Management Licensing Regulations 1994.

(**b**) 1985 c.6; section 736 is substituted by section 144(1) of the Companies Act 1989 (c.40).

(b) references to the consignor were references—

    (i) in relation to the case mentioned in regulation 6(1)(b), to the person to whom the product or material was supplied; and

    (ii) in relation to the case mentioned in regulation 6(1)(d), to the master of the ship; and

(c) references to the consignee were references, in relation to the case mentioned in regulation 6(1)(b), to the person to whom the product or material is to be returned.

Consignment notes: carrier's rounds

8.—(1) This regulation applies to a carrier's round or to a succession of such rounds by the same carrier starting and ending within a twelve month period in respect of which:

(a) every consignor is a person specified in the consignment note or in the schedule prepared in accordance with paragraph (2)(b)(iii) or whose particulars are notified in writing to the Agency not less than 72 hours before the removal of the first waste on the carrier's round;

(b) the premises from which the special waste is removed are:

    (i) specified in the consignment note or in the schedule prepared in accordance with paragraph (2)(b)(iii) or notified in writing to the Agency not less than 72 hours before the removal of the first waste on the carrier's round; and

    (ii) so located that the Agency for each of those premises is the same;

(c) the special waste is of a description specified in the consignment note; and

(d) in the case of a single round other than a round that satisfies the requirements of regulation 14(2)(a), the time between the collection of the first consignment and delivery to the consignee is no more than 24 hours.

(2) Before the first removal of waste, the carrier shall,

(a) on any carrier's round which is not in a succession or on the first round in such a succession, ensure that

    (i) Parts A and B of the consignment note are completed and that the relevant code is entered;

    (ii) one copy of the consignment note is furnished to the Agency for the place to which the special waste is to be transported;

(b) on every round—

    (i) prepare four copies of the consignment note in addition to one copy for each consignor from whom waste is to be collected during the round;

    (ii) complete on those copies Parts A and B, the carrier's particulars and particulars of transport in Part C, the code assigned or supplied under regulation 4 in respect of the round and, if it is a second or subsequent round, the code in respect of the first round; and

    (iii) ensure that four copies of a schedule are prepared in the form set out in Part II of Schedule 1 to these Regulations, or in a form substantially to the like effect, in addition to one consignor's copy for each site from which waste is to be collected during that round.

(3) The consignor shall, before the removal of waste from a site, complete on all the copies that part of the schedule indicated on it as for completion by him.

(4) The carrier shall ensure, before the removal of the waste, that—

(a) the part of the schedule indicated on it as for completion by him is completed on all the copies; and

(b) he has all copies of the schedule (on which the part to be completed by the consignor has been completed) except the copy to be retained by the consignor under paragraph (5).

(5) The consignor shall retain in respect of each site one copy of the consignment note and of that part of the schedule on which the parts to be completed by him and by the carrier have been completed.

(6) The carrier shall ensure that the copies of the consignment note and of the schedule which he has received—

    (a) are completed with respect to that round;

    (b) travel with the waste to which they refer;

    (c) are given to the consignee on delivery of the waste.

(7) Subject to regulation 10, on receiving the waste collected on each round, the consignee shall—

    (a) complete Part E on the three copies of the consignment note given to him;

    (b) retain one copy of the consignment note and one copy of the schedule;

    (c) give to the carrier a copy of the consignment note and a copy of the schedule; and

    (d) forthwith furnish to the Agency for the place to which the consignment has been transported one copy of the consignment note and one copy of the schedule.

(8) The carrier shall retain the copies given to him in accordance with paragraph (7)(c).

Consignment notes: removal of ships' waste to reception facilities

9.—(1) This regulation applies where special waste is removed from a ship in a harbour area to—

    (a) reception facilities provided within that harbour area; or

    (b) by pipeline to any such facilities provided outside a harbour area.

(2) Before the waste is removed from the ship—

    (a) three copies of the consignment note shall be prepared and Parts A and B shall be completed and the relevant code entered on each of those copies;

    (b) the operator of the facilities shall complete Part C on each of those copies; and

    (c) the master of the ship—

        (i) shall ensure that Part D is completed on each of those copies;

        (ii) shall retain one copy (on which Parts A to D have been completed); and

        (iii) shall give the two remaining copies (on which Parts A to D have been completed) to the operator of the facilities.

(3) On receiving a consignment of special waste the operator of the facilities shall—

    (a) complete Part E on the copies of the consignment note which he has received;

    (b) retain one copy; and

    (c) forthwith furnish the other copy to the Agency for the place where the facilities are situated.

Consignment notes etc.: duty of consignee not accepting delivery of a consignment

10.—(1) This regulation applies where the consignee does not accept delivery of a consignment of special waste.

(2) In a case to which this regulation applies the requirements of regulation 5(4) (including that paragraph as applied in cases to which regulation 6 applies) or 8(7), as the case may be, shall not apply to the consignee.

(3) If, in a case to which this regulation applies, copies of the consignment note have been given to the consignee he shall—

    (a) indicate on Part E of each copy that he does not accept the consignment and the reasons why he does not accept the consignment;

    (b) retain one copy;

    (c) ensure that one copy, accompanied by one copy of any carrier's schedule given to him in accordance with regulation 8, are furnished forthwith to the Agency for the place to which the special waste has been transported; and

    (d) ensure that the other copy is returned to the carrier forthwith.

(4) If, in a case to which this regulation applies, no copies of the consignment note have been given to the consignee he shall ensure that a written explanation of his reasons for not accepting delivery, including such details of the consignment and of the carrier as are known to him, is furnished forthwith to the Agency for the place to which the special waste has been transported.

(5) In a case to which this regulation applies—

    (a) on being informed that the consignee will not accept delivery of the consignment, the carrier shall inform the Agency and seek instructions from the consignor;

    (b) the consignor shall forthwith inform the carrier and the Agency of his intentions as regards the consignment; and

    (c) the carrier shall take all reasonable steps to ensure that the consignor's intentions are fulfilled.

(6) For the purposes of paragraph (5), the consignor may propose one of the following, namely—

    (a) the delivery of the consignment to the premises from which it had been collected;

    (b) the delivery of the consignment to the premises at which it had been produced;

    (c) the delivery of the consignment to other specified premises in respect of which there is held any waste management licence necessary to authorise the receipt of the waste.

Consignment notes: duties of the Agencies

11.—(1) Subject to paragraph (2), where—

    (a) an Agency ("the receiving Agency") has been furnished with a copy of a consignment note under regulation 5, 7, 8, 9 or 10 or with a copy of the explanation under regulation 10(4); and

    (b) the other Agency is the Agency for the premises from which the special waste was removed,

the receiving Agency shall, within two weeks of receipt, send to the other Agency one copy of the consignment note or explanation as the case may be.

(2) Where copies have been furnished—

    (a) under regulation 7 in a case to which regulation 6 applies by virtue of paragraph (1)(d) of that regulation, or

    (b) under regulation 9(3)(c),

paragraph (1) shall have effect as if the reference to the premises from which the special waste was removed were a reference to the harbour area in which the special waste was removed from the ship.

Consignment notes: provisions as to furnishing

12.—(1) Subject to paragraphs (2), (3) and (6), a copy of a consignment note required by regulation 5 or 8 to be furnished to an Agency must be furnished not more than one month and not less than 72 hours before the removal of the consignment.

(2) Subject to paragraphs (3) and (6), a copy of a consignment note required to be furnished by regulation 8(2)(a)(ii) shall be furnished not less than 72 hours before the removal of the first consignment to which the consignment note relates.

(3) The copy of the consignment note mentioned in paragraphs (1) and (2) may be furnished to the Agency within 72 hours before the removal where—

    (a) the consignment is to be delivered to other specified premises pursuant to a proposal under regulation 10(6)(c);

    (b) the consignment cannot lawfully remain where it is for 72 hours.

(4) The requirements of paragraphs (1) and (2) shall be treated as satisfied if—

(a) a facsimile of the copy is furnished to the Agency by telephonic, electronic or other similar means of transmission in compliance with the time limits set out in those paragraphs, and

(b) the copy is furnished to the Agency before or, in accordance with paragraph (5) below, forthwith upon removal of the consignment.

(5) A copy of a consignment note or a written explanation of reasons for refusing to accept delivery of any special waste is furnished to an Agency in accordance with this paragraph if it, and any document required to be furnished with it, is—

(a) delivered to the Agency, or

(b) posted to the Agency by pre-paid first class post,

within one day of the receipt, removal or refusal to accept delivery of the special waste in question, as the case may be.

(6) In reckoning any period of hours for the purposes of paragraphs (1), (2) and (3), the hours of any Saturday, Sunday, Good Friday, Christmas Day, bank holiday or other public holiday shall be disregarded.

Consignment notes: importers and exporters

13.—(1) Subject to paragraphs (3) and (4), regulations 5 to 12 shall apply to special waste imported into Great Britain from Northern Ireland or Gibraltar as if—

(a) any reference to the consignor were a reference to the person importing the special waste;

(b) any reference to the premises at which the special waste is being held and from which it is removed were a reference to the place where it first enters Great Britain; and

(c) the special waste is removed from that place at the time when it first enters Great Britain.

(2) Subject to paragraph (4), these Regulations shall apply to special waste exported from Great Britain to Northern Ireland or Gibraltar as if—

(a) any reference to the consignee were a reference to the person exporting the waste; and

(b) the consignment of special waste is received by that person at the place where and the time when it leaves Great Britain.

(3) Paragraph (1) does not apply in a case to which either regulation 6(1)(d) or regulation 9 applies.

(4) Nothing in regulations 5 to 12 shall apply in relation to shipments of waste to which the provisions of Council Regulation (EEC) No. 259/93(a), other than Title III of that Regulation, apply.

Fees

14.—(1) Subject to paragraph (2), when it assigns or supplies a code for a consignment or a carrier's round in accordance with regulation 4(1), an Agency shall require payment of a fee of—

(a) £10 in respect of a code relating to a consignment, or a round, which consists entirely of lead acid motor vehicle batteries;

(b) £15 in other cases.

(a) OJ No. L 30, 6.2.1993, p.1.

(2) An Agency shall not require payment of a fee where the code is assigned or supplied in connection with:

    (a) a second or subsequent carrier's round in a succession of such rounds, in respect of which—

        (i) the carrier is also the consignee in relation to every consignment in all the rounds;

        (ii) no more than one consignment is collected from any consignor during the succession;

        (iii) the total weight of special waste collected in each round does not exceed 400 kg; and

        (iv) the time between the collection of the first consignment on the first round in the succession and the delivery of the last consignment to the place to which it is to be transported is no more than one week.

    (b) the removal of a single consignment of special waste for the purposes set out in regulation 6(1)(b) provided that the person to whom the product or material was supplied is satisfied that it fails to meet any specification which he expected it to meet; or

    (c) the removal of special waste from a ship in a harbour area—

        (i) to a conveyance for transportation to a place outside that area;

        (ii) to reception facilities provided within the same harbour area; or

        (iii) by pipeline to reception facilities provided outside the harbour area.

Registers

15.—(1) At each site from which any consignment of special waste has been removed, the consignor shall keep a register containing—

    (a) a copy of the consignment note; and

    (b) where the consignment is one to which regulation 8 applies, a copy of that part of the carrier's schedule retained under regulation 8(5),

applicable to each consignment removed from that site.

(2) Every carrier shall keep a register containing—

    (a) a copy of the consignment note; and

    (b) where the consignment is one to which regulation 8 applies, a copy of the carrier's schedule,

applicable to each consignment which he has transported.

(3) At each site at which any consignment of special waste has been received, the consignee shall keep a register containing—

    (a) a copy of the consignment note; and

    (b) where the consignment is one to which regulation 8 applies, a copy of the carrier's schedule,

applicable to each consignment, other than a consignment to which regulation 10 applies, received at that site.

(4) A consignment note or carrier's schedule required by paragraph (1) or (2) to be kept in a register shall be retained in the register for not less than three years from the date on which the waste to which it relates was removed from the premises at which it was being held.

(5) Subject to paragraphs (6) and (7), consignment notes and carrier's schedules required by paragraph (3) to be kept by a person shall be retained until his waste management licence for the site in question is surrendered or revoked entirely, at which time he shall send the register to the Agency for the site; and that Agency shall retain the register for not less than three years after its receipt.

(6) Where, by virtue of regulation 16(1)(a) or (b) of the 1994 Regulations, section 33(1)(a), (b) and (c) of the 1990 Act does not apply to any of the activities carried on at a site at which special waste is received, paragraph (5) shall have effect as if any reference to the surrender or revocation of a person's waste management licence were a reference to the surrender or revocation of his authorisation under Part I of the 1990 Act for the site in question.

(7) Where, in circumstances other than those mentioned in paragraph (6), section 33(1)(a) and (b) of the 1990 Act does not apply to any of the activities carried on at a site at which special waste is received, each consignment note and carrier's schedule required to be kept in a register shall be kept in that register for not less than three years from the date on which the consignment of special waste to which it relates was received at the site to which it was transported.

(8) Insofar as is consistent with the foregoing provisions of this regulation, registers under this regulation may be kept in any form.

Site records

16.—(1) Any person who makes a deposit of special waste in or on any land shall record the location of each such deposit, shall keep such records until his waste management licence is surrendered or revoked and shall then send the records to the Agency for the site.

(2) Such records shall comprise either—

(a) a site plan marked with a grid, or

(b) a site plan with overlays on which deposits are shown in relation to the contours of the site.

(3) Deposits shall be described in such records by reference to the register of consignment notes kept under regulation 15, save that where waste is disposed of—

(a) by pipeline, or

(b) within the curtilage of the premises at which it is produced,

the deposits shall be described by reference to a record of the quantity and composition of the waste and the date of its disposal.

(4) In the case of liquid wastes discharged without containers into underground strata or disused workings the record shall comprise only a written statement of the quantity and composition of special waste so discharged and the date of its disposal.

(5) Every record made pursuant to regulation 14 of the Control of Pollution (Special Waste) Regulations 1980(a) shall—

(a) be kept with the records referred to in paragraph (1) above for so long as is mentioned in that paragraph, and

(b) shall accompany those records when they are sent to the Agency in accordance with that paragraph.

Restrictions on mixing special waste

17.—(1) Subject to paragraph (2), an establishment or undertaking which carries out the disposal or recovery of special waste, or which collects or transports special waste, shall not—

(a) mix different categories of special waste; or

(b) mix special waste with waste which is not special waste.

(2) Paragraph (1) above shall not apply if the mixing—

(a) is authorised by a waste management licence or under an authorisation granted under Part I of the 1990 Act; or

(b) is an activity to which, by virtue of regulation 17 of the 1994 Regulations, section 33(1)(a) and (b) of the 1990 Act does not apply.

(a) S.I. 1980/1709, as amended by S.I. 1988/1562, 1988/1790, 1994/1137 and by Part IV of Schedule 6 to the Radioactive Substances Act 1993 (c.12).

Offences

18.—(1) Subject to paragraph (2) below, it shall be an offence for a person (other than a member, officer or employee of an Agency who is acting as authorised by that Agency,) to fail to comply with any of the foregoing provisions of these Regulations insofar as that provision imposes any obligation or requirement upon him.

(2) It shall be a defence for a person charged with an offence under paragraph (1) to prove that he was not reasonably able to comply with the provision in question by reason of an emergency or grave danger and that he took all steps as were reasonably practicable in the circumstances for—

(a) minimising any threat to the public or the environment; and

(b) ensuring that the provision in question was complied with as soon as reasonably practicable after the event.

(3) A person who, in purported compliance with a requirement imposed by or under any of the foregoing provisions of these Regulations to furnish any information, makes a statement which he knows to be false or misleading in a material particular, or recklessly makes any statement which is false or misleading in a material particular, commits an offence.

(4) A person who intentionally makes a false entry in any record or register required to be kept by virtue of any of the foregoing provisions of these Regulations commits an offence.

(5) Where the commission by any person of an offence under this regulation is due to the act or default of some other person, that other person may be charged with and convicted of an offence by virtue of this paragraph whether or not proceedings are taken against the first-mentioned person.

(6) Where an offence under this regulation which has been committed by a body corporate is proved to have been committed with the consent or connivance of, or to have been attributable to, any neglect on the part of a director, manager, secretary or other similar officer of the body corporate, or any person who was purporting to act in any such capacity, he, as well as the body corporate, shall be liable to be proceeded against and punished accordingly.

(7) Where the affairs of a body corporate are managed by its members, paragraph (6) shall apply in relation to the acts or defaults of a member in connection with his functions of management as if he were a director of the body corporate.

(8) Where, in Scotland, an offence under this regulation which has been committed by a partnership or an unincorporated association (other than a partnership) is proved to have been committed with the consent or connivance of, or to have been attributable to any neglect on the part of, a partner in the partnership or, as the case may be, a person concerned in the management or control of the association, he, as well as the partnership or association, shall be liable to be proceeded against and punished accordingly.

(9) A person who commits an offence under this regulation shall be liable—

(a) on summary conviction, to a fine not exceeding level 5 on the standard scale;

(b) on conviction on indictment, to a fine or to imprisonment for a term not exceeding two years, or to both.

Responsibilities of the Agencies

19. The Agencies shall be responsible for supervising the persons and activities subject to any provision of these Regulations.

Transitional provisions for certificates of technical competence

20.—(1) This regulation applies in relation to—

(a) waste defined as special waste under regulation 2 of these Regulations which was not so defined under regulation 2 of the Control of Pollution (Special Waste) Regulations 1980**(a)** ("waste now defined as special waste"); and

(b) persons to be treated as technically competent for the purposes of section 74(3)(b) of the 1990 Act—

  (i) pursuant to regulation 4 of the 1994 Regulations; or

  (ii) pursuant to regulation 5 of the 1994 Regulations, or to regulation 4(1) or (3) of the Waste Management Licensing (Amendment etc.) Regulations 1995**(b)**.

(2) For the purposes only of operations concerning waste now defined as special waste and provided that both the conditions set out in paragraph (3) are satisfied, the persons referred to in paragraph (1)(b) shall continue to be treated as technically competent—

(a) in the case of those referred to in paragraph (1)(b)(i), until 10th August 2000; and

(b) in the case of those referred to in paragraph (1)(b)(ii), in accordance with the Regulations mentioned there, except that paragraph (1) of regulation 5 of the 1994 Regulations and paragraphs (1) and (4) of regulation 4 of the Waste Management Licensing (Amendment etc.) Regulations 1995 shall have effect as if for the date "10th August 1999" there were substituted the date "10th August 2000".

(3) The conditions referred to in paragraph (2) are that:

(a) before 1st March 1997, the person applies to the Waste Management Industry Training and Advisory Board for a certificate of technical competence at Level 4 in respect of special waste; and

(b) before 1st September 1996, the person was entitled to act as the manager of a facility in respect of which there was in force a waste management licence authorising activities concerning waste now defined as special waste.

Amendment of regulations relating to the assessment of environmental effects

21.—(1) In regulation 2(1) of the Town and Country Planning (Assessment of Environmental Effects) Regulations 1988**(c)**, for the definition of "special waste" there shall be substituted—

" "special waste" means waste which is special waste for the purposes of the Special Waste Regulations 1996;".

(2) In regulation 4(1) of the Environmental Assessment (Scotland) Regulations 1988**(d)**, for the definition of "special waste" there shall be substituted—

" "special waste" means waste which is special waste for the purposes of the Special Waste Regulations 1996;".

Amendment of the Controlled Waste (Registration of Carriers and Seizure of Vehicles) Regulations 1991

22. In Schedule 1 to the Controlled Waste (Registration of Carriers and Seizure of Vehicles) Regulations 1991**(e)** there shall be added at the end—

"the Special Waste Regulations 1996".

(a) S.I. 1980/1709, amended by S.I. 1988/1790.
(b) S.I. 1995/288, amended by S.I. 1995/1950. Paragraph (3) of regulation 4 is subject to paragraphs (4) and (5), the latter being inserted by regulation 3 of S.I. 1995/1950 and amended by regulation 3 of S.I. 1996/634.
(c) S.I. 1988/1199, to which there are amendments not relevant to these Regulations.
(d) S.I. 1988/1221.
(e) S.I. 1991/1624, to which there are amendments not relevant to these Regulations.

Amendment of the Environmental Protection (Duty of Care) Regulations 1991

23. In regulation 2 of the Environmental Protection (Duty of Care) Regulations 1991(a)—

(a) at the beginning of paragraph (1), there shall be added "Subject to paragraph (3),";

(b) after paragraph (2), the following paragraph shall be added:

"(3) Paragraph (1) shall not apply where the waste transferred is special waste within the meaning of the Special Waste Regulations 1996 and the consignment note and, where appropriate, schedule required by those Regulations are completed and dealt with in accordance with those Regulations.".

Amendment of the Controlled Waste Regulations 1992

24. In paragraph 18(2) of Schedule 3 to the Controlled Waste Regulations 1992(b), for the definition of "tank washings", there shall be substituted—

" "tank washings" has the same meaning as in paragraph 36 of Schedule 3 to the Waste Management Licensing Regulations 1994;".

Amendment of the Waste Management Licensing Regulations 1994

25. The 1994 Regulations shall be amended in accordance with Schedule 3 to these Regulations.

Revocations and savings

26.—(1) Subject to paragraph (2), the following are hereby revoked—

(a) the Control of Pollution (Special Waste) Regulations 1980(c) ("the 1980 Regulations");

(b) the Control of Pollution (Landed Ships' Waste) Regulations 1987(d);

(c) the Control of Pollution (Landed Ships' Waste) (Amendment) Regulations 1989(e); and

(d) paragraphs (1) and (2) of regulation 18 of the Transfrontier Shipment of Waste Regulations 1994(f).

(2) Subject to paragraph (3) of this regulation, the 1980 Regulations shall continue to have effect in relation to any special waste in respect of which the consignment note (within the meaning of those Regulations) was furnished or is treated as having been furnished to the Agency, in accordance with regulation 4 of those Regulations, before the coming into force of these Regulations.

(3) Paragraph (2) of this regulation shall not apply in relation to any special waste in respect of which consignment notes or copies of consignment notes are furnished pursuant to regulation 9 of the 1980 Regulations and after 31st August 1996 any direction made under regulation 9 of the 1980 Regulations shall have no effect.

Ferrers
Minister of State,
Department of the Environment

28th March 1996

Gwilym Jones
Parliamentary Under-Secretary of State,
Welsh Office

28th March 1996

Lindsay
Parliamentary Under-Secretary of State,
Scottish Office

28th March 1996

(a) S.I. 1991/2839.
(b) S.I. 1992/588, as amended by S.I. 1993/566, 1994/1056 and 1995/288.
(c) S.I. 1980/1709, as amended by S.I. 1988/1562, 1988/1790 and 1994/1137 and by Part IV of Schedule 6 to the Radioactive Substances Act 1993 (c.12).
(d) S.I. 1987/402.
(e) S.I. 1989/65.
(f) S.I. 1994/1137.

SPECIAL WASTE REGULATIONS 1996

Nº of prenotice *(if different)* _____

Consignment Note Nº _____

Sheet _____ of _____

A   CONSIGNMENT DETAILS

PLEASE TICK IF YOU ARE A TRANSFER STATION ☐

1. The waste described below is to be removed from (name, address and postcode)

2. The waste will be taken to (address & postcode)

3. The consignment(s) will be: one single ☐   a succession ☐   carrier's round ☐   other ☐

4. Expected removal date of first consignment: last consignment:

5. Name   On behalf of (company)
   Signature   Date

6. ☎   7. The waste producer was (if different from 1)

B   DESCRIPTION OF THE WASTE   Nº of additional sheet(s) ☐

1. The waste is   2. Classification

3. Physical Form: Liquid ☐   Powder ☐   Sludge ☐   Solid ☐   Mixed ☐   4. Colour

5. Total quantity for removal   quantity   units (eg kg/ltrs/tonnes)   Container type, number and size:

6. The chemical/biological components that make the waste special are:

Component	Concentration (% or mg/kg)	Component	Concentration (% or mg/kg)

7. The hazards are:

8. The process giving rise to waste is:

C   CARRIER'S CERTIFICATE   I certify that I today collected the consignment and that the details in A1, A2 and B1 above are correct. The Quantity collected in the load is:

Name   On behalf of (company) (name & address)

Signature   Date   at   hrs.

1. Carrier registration nº/reason for exemption   2. Vehicle registration nº (or mode of transport, if not road)

D   CONSIGNOR'S CERTIFICATE

I certify that the information in B and C above are correct, that the carrier is registered or exempt and was advised of the appropriate precautionary measures.

Name   On behalf of (company)

Signature   Date

E   CONSIGNEE'S CERTIFICATE

1. I received this waste on   at   hrs.   2. Quantity received   quantity   units (eg kg/ltrs/tonnes)

3. Vehicle registration nº   4. Management Operation

I certify that waste management licence /authorisation/exemption nº   authorises the management of the waste described in B.

Name   On behalf of (company)

Signature   Date

FED 1041 (03/96 DDP)

PART II

FORM OF SCHEDULE

SPECIAL WASTE REGULATIONS 1996: CARRIER SCHEDULE   Consignment Note Nº _____

Sheet   of

Name and address of premises from which waste was removed	I certify that today I collected the quantity of waste shown from the address given here and will take it to the address given in A2 on the consignment note
	Quantity of waste removed · Carrier's signature and Date
	I certify that the waste collected is as detailed above and conforms with the description given in B on the relevant consignment note
Consignment Note Nº	Name of Consignor · Signature and Date

Name and address of premises from which waste was removed	I certify that today I collected the quantity of waste shown from the address given here and will take it to the address given in A2 on the consignment note
	Quantity of waste removed · Carrier's signature and Date
	I certify that the waste collected is as detailed above and conforms with the description given in B on the relevant consignment note
Consignment Note Nº	Name of Consignor · Signature and Date

Name and address of premises from which waste was removed	I certify that today I collected the quantity of waste shown from the address given here and will take it to the address given in A2 on the consignment note
	Quantity of waste removed · Carrier's signature and Date
	I certify that the waste collected is as detailed above and conforms with the description given in B on the relevant consignment note
Consignment Note Nº	Name of Consignor · Signature and Date

Name and address of premises from which waste was removed	I certify that today I collected the quantity of waste shown from the address given here and will take it to the address given in A2 on the consignment note
	Quantity of waste removed · Carrier's signature and Date
	I certify that the waste collected is as detailed above and conforms with the description given in B on the relevant consignment note
Consignment Note Nº	Name of Consignor · Signature and Date

Name and address of premises from which waste was removed	I certify that today I collected the quantity of waste shown from the address given here and will take it to the address given in A2 on the consignment note
	Quantity of waste removed · Carrier's signature and Date
	I certify that the waste collected is as detailed above and conforms with the description given in B on the relevant consignment note
Consignment Note Nº	Name of Consignor · Signature and Date

Name and address of premises from which waste was removed	I certify that today I collected the quantity of waste shown from the address given here and will take it to the address given in A2 on the consignment note
	Quanity of waste removed · Carrier's signature and Date
	I certify that the waste collected is as detailed above and conforms with the description given in B on the relevant consignment note
Consignment Note Nº	Name of Consignor · Signature and Date

FED 1091 (03/96 DDP)

SPECIAL WASTE

PART I

HAZARDOUS WASTE LIST

Waste code (6 digits)/ Chapter Heading (2 and 4 digits)	Description
02	WASTE FROM AGRICULTURAL, HORTICULTURAL, HUNTING, FISHING AND AQUACULTURE PRIMARY PRODUCTION, FOOD PREPARATION AND PROCESSING
0201	PRIMARY PRODUCTION WASTE
020105	agrochemical wastes
03	WASTES FROM WOOD PROCESSING AND THE PRODUCTION OF PAPER, CARDBOARD, PULP, PANELS AND FURNITURE
0302	WOOD PRESERVATION WASTE
030201	non-halogenated organic wood preservatives
030202	organochlorinated wood preservatives
030203	organometallic wood preservatives
030204	inorganic wood preservatives
04	WASTES FROM THE LEATHER AND TEXTILE INDUSTRIES
0401	WASTES FROM THE LEATHER INDUSTRY
040103	degreasing wastes containing solvents without a liquid phase
0402	WASTES FROM TEXTILE INDUSTRY
040211	halogenated wastes from dressing and finishing
05	WASTES FROM PETROLEUM REFINING, NATURAL GAS PURIFICATION AND PYROLYTIC TREATMENT OF COAL
0501	OILY SLUDGES AND SOLID WASTES
050103	tank bottom sludges
050104	acid alkyl sludges
050105	oil spills
050107	acid tars
050108	other tars
0504	SPENT FILTER CLAYS
050401	spent filter clays
0506	WASTE FROM THE PYROLYTIC TREATMENT OF COAL
050601	acid tars
050603	other tars
0507	WASTE FROM NATURAL GAS PURIFICATION
050701	sludges containing mercury
0508	WASTES FROM OIL REGENERATION
050801	spent filter clays
050802	acid tars
050803	other tars
050804	aqueous liquid waste from oil regeneration
06	WASTES FROM INORGANIC CHEMICAL PROCESSES
0601	WASTE ACIDIC SOLUTIONS
060101	sulphuric acid and sulphurous acid
060102	hydrochloric acid
060103	hydrofluoric acid
060104	phosphoric and phosphorous acid
060105	nitric acid and nitrous acid
060199	waste not otherwise specified

Waste code (6 digits)/ Chapter Heading (2 and 4 digits)	Description
0602	ALKALINE SOLUTIONS
060201	calcium hydroxide
060202	soda
060203	ammonia
060299	wastes not otherwise specified
0603	WASTE SALTS AND THEIR SOLUTIONS
060311	salts and solutions containing cyanides
0604	METAL-CONTAINING WASTES
060402	metallic salts (except 0603)
060403	wastes containing arsenic
060404	wastes containing mercury
060405	wastes containing heavy metals
0607	WASTES FROM HALOGEN CHEMICAL PROCESSES
060701	wastes containing asbestos from electrolysis
060702	activated carbon from chlorine production
0613	WASTES FROM OTHER INORGANIC CHEMICAL PROCESSES
061301	inorganic pesticides, biocides and wood preserving agents
061302	spent activated carbon (except 060702)
07	WASTES FROM ORGANIC CHEMICAL PROCESSES
0701	WASTE FROM THE MANUFACTURE, FORMULATION, SUPPLY AND USE (MFSU) OF BASIC ORGANIC CHEMICALS
070101	aqueous washing liquids and mother liquors
070103	organic halogenated solvents, washing liquids and mother liquors
070104	other organic solvents, washing liquids and mother liquors
070107	halogenated still bottoms and reaction residues
070108	other still bottoms and reaction residues
070109	halogenated filter cakes, spent absorbents
070110	other filter cakes, spent absorbents
0702	WASTE FROM THE MFSU OF PLASTICS, SYNTHETIC RUBBER AND MAN-MADE FIBRES
070201	aqueous washing liquids and mother liquors
070203	organic halogenated solvents, washing liquids and mother liquors
070204	other organic solvents, washing liquids and mother liquors
070207	halogenated still bottoms and reaction residues
070208	other still bottoms and reaction residues
070209	halogenated filter cakes, spent absorbents
070210	other filter cakes, spent absorbents
0703	WASTE FROM THE MFSU FOR ORGANIC DYES AND PIGMENTS (EXCLUDING 0611)
070301	aqueous washing liquids and mother liquors
070303	organic halogenated solvents, washing liquids and mother liquors
070304	other organic solvents, washing liquids and mother liquors
070307	halogenated still bottoms and reaction residues
070308	other still bottoms and reaction residues
070309	halogenated filter cakes, spent absorbents
070310	other filter cakes, spent absorbents
0704	WASTE FROM THE MFSU FOR ORGANIC PESTICIDES (EXCEPT 020105)
070401	aqueous washing liquids and mother liquors
070403	organic halogenated solvents, washing liquids and mother liquors

070404	other organic solvents, washing liquids and mother liquors
070407	halogenated still bottoms and reaction residues
070408	other still bottoms and reaction residues
070409	halogenated filter cakes, spent absorbents
070410	other filter cakes, spent absorbents
0705	WASTE FROM THE MFSU OF PHARMACEUTICALS
070501	aqueous washing liquids and mother liquors
070503	organic halogenated solvents, washing liquids and mother liquors
070504	other organic solvents, washing liquids and mother liquors
070507	halogenated still bottoms and reaction residues
070508	other still bottoms and reaction residues
070509	halogenated filter cakes, spent absorbents
070510	other filter cakes, spent absorbents
0706	WASTE FROM THE MFSU OF FATS, GREASE, SOAPS, DETERGENTS, DISINFECTANTS AND COSMETICS
070601	aqueous washing liquids and mother liquors
070603	organic halogenated solvents, washing liquids and mother liquors
070604	other organic solvents, washing liquids and mother liquors
070607	halogenated still bottoms and reaction residues
070608	other still bottoms and reaction residues
070609	halogenated filter cakes, spent absorbents
070610	other filter cakes, spent absorbents
0707	WASTE FROM THE MFSU OF FINE CHEMICALS AND CHEMICAL PRODUCTS NOT OTHERWISE SPECIFIED
070701	aqueous washing liquids and mother liquors
070703	organic halogenated solvents, washing liquids and mother liquors
070704	other organic solvents, washing liquids and mother liquors
070707	halogenated still bottoms and reaction residues
070708	other still bottoms and reaction residues
070709	halogenated filter cakes, spent absorbents
070710	other filter cakes, spent absorbents
08	WASTES FROM THE MANUFACTURE, FORMULATION, SUPPLY AND USE (MFSU) OF COATINGS (PAINTS, VARNISHES AND VITREOUS ENAMELS), ADHESIVE, SEALANTS AND PRINTING INKS
0801	WASTES FROM MFSU OF PAINT AND VARNISH
080101	waste paints and varnish containing halogenated solvents
080102	waste paints and varnish free of halogenated solvents
080106	sludges from paint or varnish removal containing halogenated solvents
080107	sludges from paint or varnish removal free of halogenated solvents
0803	WASTES FROM MFSU OF PRINTING INKS
080301	waste ink containing halogenated solvents
080302	waste ink free of halogenated solvents
080305	ink sludges containing halogenated solvents
080306	ink sludges free of halogenated solvents
0804	WASTES FROM MFSU OF ADHESIVE AND SEALANTS (INCLUDING WATER-PROOFING PRODUCTS)
080401	waste adhesives and sealants containing halogenated solvents
080402	waste adhesives and sealants free of halogenated solvents
080405	adhesives and sealants sludges containing halogenated solvents
080406	adhesives and sealants sludges free of halogenated solvents

Waste code (6 digits)/ Chapter Heading (2 and 4 digits)	Description
09	WASTES FROM THE PHOTOGRAPHIC INDUSTRY
0901	WASTES FROM PHOTOGRAPHIC INDUSTRY
090101	water based developer and activator solutions
090102	water based offset plate developer solutions
090103	solvent based developer solutions
090104	fixer solutions
090105	bleach solutions and bleach fixer solutions
090106	waste containing silver from on-site treatment of photographic waste
10	INORGANIC WASTES FROM THERMAL PROCESSES
1001	WASTES FROM POWER STATION AND OTHER COMBUSTION PLANTS (EXCEPT 1900)
100104	oil fly ash
100109	sulphuric acid
1003	WASTES FROM ALUMINIUM THERMAL METALLURGY
100301	tars and other carbon-containing wastes from anode manufacture
100303	skimmings
100304	primary smelting slags/white drosses
100307	spent pot lining
100308	salt slags from secondary smelting
100309	black drosses from secondary smelting
100310	waste from treatment of salt slags and black drosses treatment
1004	WASTES FROM LEAD THERMAL METALLURGY
100401	slags (1st and 2nd smelting)
100402	dross and skimmings (1st and 2nd smelting)
100403	calcium arsenate
100404	flue gas dust
100405	other particulates and dust
100406	solid waste from gas treatment
100407	sludges from gas treatment
1005	WASTES FROM ZINC THERMAL METALLURGY
100501	slags (1st and 2nd smelting)
100502	dross and skimmings (1st and 2nd smelting)
100503	flue gas dust
100505	solid waste from gas treatment
100506	sludges from gas treatment
1006	WASTES FROM COPPER THERMAL METALLURGY
100603	flue gas dust
100605	waste from electrolytic refining
100606	solid waste from gas treatment
100607	sludges from gas treatment
11	INORGANIC WASTE WITH METALS FROM METAL TREATMENT AND THE COATING OF METALS; NON-FERROUS HYDRO-METALLURGY
1101	LIQUID WASTES AND SLUDGES FROM METAL TREATMENT AND COATING OF METALS (e.g. GALVANIC PROCESSES, ZINC COATING PROCESSES, PICKLING PROCESSES, ETCHING, PHOSPHATIZING, ALKALINE DE-GREASING)
110101	cyanidic (alkaline) wastes containing heavy metals other than chromium
110102	cyanidic (alkaline) wastes which do not contain heavy metals
110103	cyanide-free wastes containing chromium

Waste code (6 digits)/ Chapter Heading (2 and 4 digits)	Description
110105	acidic pickling solutions
110106	acids not otherwise specified
110107	alkalis not otherwise specified
110108	phosphatizing sludges
1102	WASTES AND SLUDGES FROM NON-FERROUS HYDROMETALLURGICAL PROCESSES
110202	sludges from zinc hydrometallurgy (including jarosite, goethite)
1103	SLUDGES AND SOLIDS FROM TEMPERING PROCESSES
110301	wastes containing cyanide
110302	other wastes
12	WASTES FROM SHAPING AND SURFACE TREATMENT OF METALS AND PLASTICS
1201	WASTES FROM SHAPING (INCLUDING FORGING, WELDING, PRESSING, DRAWING, TURNING, CUTTING AND FILING)
120106	waste machining oils containing halogens (not emulsioned)
120107	waste machining oils free of halogens (not emulsioned)
120108	waste machining emulsions containing halogens
120109	waste machining emulsions free of halogens
120110	synthetic machining oils
120111	machining sludges
120112	spent waxes and fats
1203	WASTES FROM WATER AND STEAM DEGREASING PROCESSES (EXCEPT 1100)
120301	aqueous washing liquids
120302	steam degreasing wastes
13	OIL WASTES (EXCEPT EDIBLE OILS, 0500 AND 1200)
1301	WASTE HYDRAULIC OILS AND BRAKE FLUIDS
130101	hydraulic oils, containing PCBs or PCTs
130102	other chlorinated hydraulic oils (not emulsions)
130103	non-chlorinated hydraulic oils (not emulsions)
130104	chlorinated emulsions
130105	non-chlorinated emulsions
130106	hydraulic oils containing only mineral oil
130107	other hydraulic oils
130108	brake fluids
1302	WASTE ENGINE, GEAR AND LUBRICATING OILS
130201	chlorinated engine, gear and lubricating oils
130202	non-chlorinated engine, gear and lubricating oils
130203	other machine, gear and lubricating oils
1303	WASTE INSULATING AND HEAT TRANSMISSION OILS AND OTHER LIQUIDS
130301	insulating or heat transmission oils and other liquids containing PCBs or PCTs
130302	other chlorinated insulating and heat transmission oils and other liquids
130303	non-chlorinated insulating and heat transmission oils and other liquids
130304	synthetic insulating and heat transmission oils and other liquids
130305	mineral insulating and heat transmission oils
1304	BILGE OILS
130401	bilge oils from inland navigation
130402	bilge oils from jetty sewers
130403	bilge oils from other navigation

Waste code (6 digits)/ Chapter Heading (2 and 4 digits)	Description
1305	OIL/WATER SEPARATOR CONTENTS
130501	oil/water separator solids
130502	oil/water separator sludges
130503	interceptor sludges
130504	desalter sludges or emulsions
130505	other emulsions
1306	OIL WASTE NOT OTHERWISE SPECIFIED
130601	oil waste not otherwise specified
14	WASTES FROM ORGANIC SUBSTANCES EMPLOYED AS SOLVENTS (EXCEPT 0700 AND 0800)
1401	WASTES FROM METAL DEGREASING AND MACHINERY MAINTENANCE
140101	chlorofluorocarbons
140102	other halogenated solvents and solvent mixes
140103	other solvents and solvent mixes
140104	aqueous solvent mixes containing halogens
140105	aqueous solvent mixes free of halogens
140106	sludges or solid wastes containing halogenated solvents
140107	sludges or solid wastes free of halogenated solvents
1402	WASTES FROM TEXTILE CLEANING AND DEGREASING OF NATURAL PRODUCTS
140201	halogenated solvents and solvent mixes
140202	solvent mixes or organic liquids free of halogenated solvents
140203	sludges or solid wastes containing halogenated solvents
140204	sludges or solid wastes containing other solvents
1403	WASTES FROM THE ELECTRONIC INDUSTRY
140301	chlorofluorocarbons
140302	other halogenated solvents
140303	solvents and solvent mixes free of halogenated solvents
140304	sludges or solid wastes containing halogenated solvents
140305	sludges or solid wastes containing other solvents
1404	WASTES FROM COOLANTS, FOAM/AEROSOL PROPELLANTS
140401	chlorofluorocarbons
140402	other halogenated solvents and solvent mixes
140403	other solvents and solvent mixes
140404	sludges or solid wastes containing halogenated solvents
140405	sludges or solid wastes containing other solvents
1405	WASTES FROM SOLVENT AND COOLANT RECOVERY (STILL BOTTOMS)
140501	chlorofluorocarbons
140502	halogenated solvents and solvent mixes
140503	other solvents and solvent mixes
140504	sludges containing halogenated solvents
140505	sludges containing other solvents
16	WASTES NOT OTHERWISE SPECIFIED IN THE CATALOGUE
1602	DISCARDED EQUIPMENT AND SHREDDER RESIDUES
160201	transformers and capacitors containing PCBs or PCTs
1604	WASTE EXPLOSIVES
160401	waste ammunition
160402	fireworks waste

Waste code (6 digits) / Chapter Heading (2 and 4 digits)	Description
160403	other waste explosives
1606	**BATTERIES AND ACCUMULATORS**
160601	lead batteries
160602	Ni-Cd batteries
160603	mercury dry cells
160606	electrolyte from batteries and accumulators
1607	**WASTE FROM TRANSPORT AND STORAGE TANK CLEANING (EXCEPT 0500 AND 1200)**
160701	waste from marine transport tank cleaning, containing chemicals
160702	waste from marine transport tank cleaning, containing oil
160703	waste from railway and road transport tank cleaning, containing oil
160704	waste from railway and road transport tank cleaning, containing chemicals
160705	waste from storage tank cleaning, containing chemicals
160706	waste from storage tank cleaning, containing oil
17	**CONSTRUCTION AND DEMOLITION WASTE (INCLUDING ROAD CONSTRUCTION)**
1706	**INSULATION MATERIALS**
170601	insulation materials containing asbestos
18	**WASTES FROM HUMAN OR ANIMAL HEALTH CARE AND/ OR RELATED RESEARCH (EXCLUDING KITCHEN AND RESTAURANT WASTES WHICH DO NOT ARISE FROM IMMEDIATE HEALTH CARE)**
1801	**WASTE FROM NATAL CARE, DIAGNOSIS, TREATMENT OR PREVENTION OF DISEASE IN HUMANS**
180103	other wastes whose collection and disposal is subject to special requirements in view of the prevention of infection
1802	**WASTE FROM RESEARCH, DIAGNOSIS, TREATMENT OR PREVENTION OF DISEASE INVOLVING ANIMALS**
180202	other wastes whose collection and disposal is subject to special requirements in view of the prevention of infection
180204	discarded chemicals
19	**WASTES FROM WASTE TREATMENT FACILITIES, OFF-SITE WASTE WATER TREATMENT PLANTS AND THE WATER INDUSTRY**
1901	**WASTES FROM INCINERATION OR PYROLYSIS OF MUNICIPAL AND SIMILAR COMMERCIAL, INDUSTRIAL AND INSTITUTIONAL WASTES**
190103	fly ash
190104	boiler dust
190105	filter cake from gas treatment
190106	aqueous liquid waste from gas treatment and other aqueous liquid wastes
190107	solid waste from gas treatment
190110	spent activated carbon from flue gas treatment
1902	**WASTES FROM SPECIFIC PHYSICO/CHEMICAL TREATMENTS OF INDUSTRIAL WASTES (e.g. DECHROMATATION, DECYANIDATION, NEUTRALIZATION)**
190201	metal hydroxide sludges and other sludges from metal insolubilization treatment
1904	**VITRIFIED WASTES AND WASTES FROM VITRIFICATION**
190402	fly ash and other flue gas treatment wastes
190403	non-vitrified solid phase

Waste code (6 digits)/ Chapter Heading (2 and 4 digits)	Description
1908	WASTES FROM WASTE WATER TREATMENT PLANTS NOT OTHERWISE SPECIFIED
190803	grease and oil mixture from oil/waste water separation
190806	saturated or spent ion exchange resins
190807	solutions and sludges from regeneration of ion exchangers
20	MUNICIPAL WASTES AND SIMILAR COMMERCIAL, INDUSTRIAL AND INSTITUTIONAL WASTES INCLUDING SEPARATELY COLLECTED FRACTIONS
2001	SEPARATELY COLLECTED FRACTIONS
200112	paint, inks, adhesives and resins
200113	solvents
200117	photo chemicals
200119	pesticides
200121	fluorescent tubes and other mercury containing waste

PART II

HAZARDOUS PROPERTIES

H1   "Explosive": substances and preparations which may explode under the effect of flame or which are more sensitive to shocks or friction than dinitrobenzene.

H2   "Oxidizing": substances and preparations which exhibit highly exothermic reactions when in contact with other substances, particularly flammable substances.

H3-A   "Highly flammable":

—liquid substances and preparations having a flash point below 21°C (including extremely flammable liquids), or

—substances and preparations which may become hot and finally catch fire in contact with air at ambient temperature without any application of energy, or

—solid substances and preparations which may readily catch fire after brief contact with a source of ignition and which continue to burn or to be consumed after removal of the source of ignition, or

—gaseous substances and preparations which are flammable in air at normal pressure, or

—substances and preparations which, in contact with water or damp air, evolve highly flammable gases in dangerous quantities.

H3-B   "Flammable": liquid substances and preparations having a flash point equal to or greater than 21°C and less than or equal to 55°C.

H4   "Irritant": non-corrosive substances and preparations which, through immediate, prolonged or repeated contact with the skin or mucous membrane, can cause inflammation.

H5   "Harmful": substances and preparations which, if they are inhaled or ingested or if they penetrate the skin, may involve limited health risks.

H6   "Toxic": substances and preparations (including very toxic substances and preparations) which, if they are inhaled or ingested or if they penetrate the skin, may involve serious, acute or chronic health risks and even death.

H7   "Carcinogenic": substances and preparations which, if they are inhaled or ingested or if they penetrate the skin, may induce cancer or increase its incidence.

H8   "Corrosive": substances and preparations which may destroy living tissue on contact.

H9   "Infectious": substances containing viable micro-organisms or their toxins which are known or reliably believed to cause disease in man or other living organisms.

H10   "Teratogenic": substances and preparations which, if they are inhaled or ingested or if they penetrate the skin, may induce non-hereditary congenital malformations or increase their incidence.

H11   "Mutagenic": substances and preparations which, if they are inhaled or ingested or if they penetrate the skin, may induce hereditary genetic defects or increase their incidence.

H12   Substances and preparations which release toxic or very toxic gases in contact with water, air or an acid.

H13   Substances and preparations capable by any means, after disposal, of yielding another substance, e.g. a leachate, which possesses any of the characteristics listed above.

H14   "Ecotoxic": substances and preparations which present or may present immediate or delayed risks for one or more sectors of the environment.

PART III
THRESHOLDS FOR CERTAIN HAZARDOUS PROPERTIES

In the waste:

—the total concentration of substances classified as irritant and having assigned to them any of the risk phrases R36 ("irritating to the eyes"), R37 ("irritating to the respiratory system") or R38 ("irritating to the skin") is equal to or greater than 20%;

—the total concentration of substances classified as irritant and having assigned to them the risk phrase R41 ("risk of serious damage to eyes") is equal to or greater than 10%;

—the total concentration of substances classified as harmful is equal to or greater than 25%;

—the total concentration of substances classified as very toxic is equal to or greater than 0.1%;

—the total concentration of substances classified as toxic is equal to or greater than 3%;

—the total concentration of substances classified as carcinogenic and placed by the approved classification and labelling guide in category 1 or 2 of that classification is equal to or greater than 0.1%;

—the total concentration of substances classified as corrosive and having assigned to them the risk phrase R34 ("causes burns") is equal to or greater than 5%; and

—the total concentration of substances classified as corrosive and having assigned to them the risk phrase R35 ("causes severe burns") is equal to or greater than 1%.

SCHEDULE 3   Regulation 25

AMENDMENTS TO THE WASTE MANAGEMENT LICENSING REGULATIONS 1994

Provision of Regulations	Amendment
regulation 1(3)	For the definition of "special waste", substitute— "special waste" has the meaning given by regulation 2 of the Special Waste Regulations 1996, except that it does not include radioactive waste within the meaning of the Radioactive Substances Act 1993;".
regulation 3	At the end of paragraph (m) add— "(n) the Special Waste Regulations 1996".
regulation 10(1)(k)	At the end add "or regulation 15(5) or 16(1) of the Special Waste Regulations 1996".
regulation 17	After paragraph (3), insert the following— "(3A) Paragraph (1) does not apply to the carrying on of an exempt activity insofar as it involves the carrying out, by an establishment or undertaking, of their own waste disposal at the place of production if the waste being disposed of is special waste.".
Schedule 3	(a) In paragraph 3(a)(ii) after "waste oil" insert "(including waste oil which is special waste)". (b) In paragraph 3(c) after "waste oil", in the first place where those words appear, insert "(including waste oil which is special waste)".

Provision of Regulations	Amendment

(c) In paragraph 18(2)(b) add at the end "(including waste oil which is special waste)".

(d) For paragraph 28 substitute—

"28. The storage of returned goods that are waste, and the secure storage of returned goods that are special waste, pending recovery or disposal, for a period not exceeding one month, by their manufacturer, distributor or retailer."

Schedule 4

(a) At the end of paragraph 9 of Part I add—

"(9) In subsection (1) of section 62, any reference to the treatment, keeping or disposal of such waste as is referred to in that subsection shall include a reference to submitting such waste to any of the operations listed in Part III or IV of this Schedule.

(10) In subsection (2) of section 62, any reference to the treatment, keeping or disposal of special waste shall include a reference to submitting special waste to any of the operations listed in Part III or IV of this Schedule.".

(b) In paragraph 13(1) of Part I after "(dealers or brokers),", insert "and producers of special waste,".

(c) At the end of paragraph 14(1)(b) of Part I add "or, in the case of special waste, to a previous holder; and for this purpose "holder", in respect of any such waste, means the producer or the person in possession of it".

(d) After paragraph 14(1) of Part I insert—

"(1A) Where special waste is recovered or disposed of by an establishment or undertaking, it shall keep a record of the carrying out and supervision of the operation and, in the case of a disposal operation, of the after-care of the disposal site."

(e) At the end of paragraph 14 of Part I(a) add—

"(4) Subject to sub-paragraph (5) below, it shall be an offence for an establishment or undertaking to fail to comply with any of the foregoing provisions of this paragraph insofar as that provision imposes any requirement or obligation upon it.

(5) Paragraph (2) of regulation 18 of the Special Waste Regulations 1996 (defence in cases of emergency etc.) shall apply to a person charged with an offence under sub-paragraph (4) above as it applies to a person charged with an offence under paragraph (1) of that regulation.

(6) A person who, in purported compliance with a requirement to furnish any information imposed by or under any of the provisions of this paragraph, makes a statement which he knows to be false or misleading in a material particular, or recklessly makes any statement which is false or misleading in a material particular, commits an offence.

(7) A person who intentionally makes a false entry in any record required to be kept by virtue of any of the provisions of this paragraph commits an offence.

(8) Paragraphs (5) to (9) of regulation 18 of the Special Waste Regulations 1996 (offence where act or default causes offence by another, offences by bodies corporate and penalties) shall apply to an offence under this paragraph as they apply to an offence under that regulation.".

Schedule 5

In Parts II and III, insert at the end of paragraph 3 of the guidance notes—

"the Special Waste Regulations 1996".

(a) Paragraph 14 is amended by regulation 3(19) to (21) of the **Waste Management Licensing (Amendment etc.) Regulations 1995** (S.I. 1995/288).

EXPLANATORY NOTE

(This note is not part of the Regulations)

These Regulations provide a new definition of special waste. They make provision for handling such waste and for implementing Council Directive 91/689/EEC on hazardous waste (OJ No. L 377, 31.12.1991, p. 20,) ("the Directive").

Regulation 2 defines special waste, making reference to Parts I, II and III of Schedule 2. This is to implement the definition of hazardous waste in the Directive and in particular in the List annexed to Council Decision 94/904/EC (OJ No. L. 356, 31.12.94, p.14). The definition extends, in accordance with Article 4 of the Directive, to certain other waste considered by the United Kingdom to display particular hazardous properties. Household waste is excluded from the definition.

Regulation 4 requires the Environment Agency (in relation to England and Wales) and the Scottish Environment Protection Agency (in relation to Scotland) ("the Agencies"), to give unique codes to be applied to consignments of waste or to carrier's rounds. Carrier's rounds consist of several consignments collected on the same journey and delivered to one place. The codes are to be shown, together with other required information, on consignment notes which are to accompany the waste when transported. Regulations 5 to 10 and 12 and 13 and Schedule 1 provide for the completion and handling of these notes and for pre-notification to the Agency of the consignment or round. Completion of such identification forms and their transport with waste are required by Article 5 of the Directive. The pre-notification provisions (regulations 5(2)(b), 8(2)(a)(ii) and 12) are not implementing specific Community obligations.

Regulation 11 requires the Agencies to provide certain information to one another, following notification, where waste is to be transported from England and Wales to Scotland or vice versa. Regulation 14 requires the Agencies to charge fees on supplying a code under regulation 4. The amount is generally £15 per consignment or round and £10 where the waste consists entirely of lead acid batteries. Rounds of low quantity fulfilling certain conditions attract no fees. Regulations 11 and 14 do not implement Community obligations.

Regulation 15 implements Article 4.3 of the Directive on the keeping of records by those consigning and carrying hazardous waste. They are both required to keep the documents for three years, although the Directive only requires carriers to keep records for at least twelve months. Together with regulation 16, it also implements the requirements of Article 2.1 of the Directive on the keeping of records for sites where hazardous waste is deposited.

Regulation 17 prohibits the mixing of special waste with other waste or other categories of special waste except where this is authorised under, or exempted from the effect of, certain other waste management legislation. This regulation is to implement Articles 2.2 and 2.3 of the Directive.

Regulation 18 makes failure to comply with the Regulations a criminal offence except for an Agency member, officer or employee. There is a defence for those who take certain steps in cases of emergency or grave danger. The Agencies are made responsible by regulation 19 for supervising activities and persons subject to the Regulations. Insofar as they relate to provisions which implement Community obligations (as stated in this Note), these provisions are part of that implementation because their purpose is to make the implementation effective.

Regulation 20 makes transitional provision for applications for certificates of technical competence under the Waste Management Licensing Regulations 1994 (S.I. 1994/1056 as amended) where such applications were made before 1st March 1997 where the applicant was licensed to deal with special waste before the change in definition made by these Regulations. This provision does not implement a Community obligation.

Regulations 21 to 26 and Schedule 3 make consequential amendments to, and revocations and saving in respect of, other legislation. Regulation 21 makes consequential amendment to regulations implementing Directive 85/337/EEC. Regulation 25 makes consequential amendment to the Waste Management Licensing Regulations 1994. Parts of those Regulations, in particular Schedule 4, implement Community obligations. Regulations 22, 23, 24 and 26 do not implement Community obligations.

A compliance cost assessment in respect of these Regulations may be obtained from Waste Policy Division (Branch 3), Department of the Environment, Room A 231, Romney House, 43 Marsham Street, London SW1P 3PY. A copy has been placed in the library of each of the Houses of Parliament.

This Statutory Instrument has been made to correct S.I. 1996/972 and is being issued free of charge to all known recipients of that Statutory Instrument

STATUTORY INSTRUMENTS

1996 No. 2019

ENVIRONMENTAL PROTECTION

The Special Waste (Amendment) Regulations 1996

Made - - - -	*1st August 1996*
Laid before Parliament	*2nd August 1996*
Coming into force	*31st August 1996*

The Secretary of State, being a Minister designated**(a)** for the purposes of section 2(2) of the European Communities Act 1972**(b)** in relation to measures relating to the regulation and control of the transit, import and export of waste (including recyclable materials) and the prevention, reduction and elimination of pollution caused by waste, in exercise of the powers conferred on him by section 2(2) of that Act, section 17 of the Control of Pollution Act 1974**(c)**, section 62(1) to (3) of the Environmental Protection Act 1990**(d)** and of all other powers enabling him in that behalf, hereby makes the following Regulations:

Citation and commencement

1. These Regulations may be cited as the Special Waste (Amendment) Regulations 1996 and shall come into force on 31st August 1996.

Amendment of the Special Waste Regulations 1996

2. The Schedule to these Regulations, which contains amendments to the Special Waste Regulations 1996**(e)**, shall have effect.

Signed by authority of the Secretary of State,

Paul Beresford
Parliamentary Under-Secretary of State,
Department of the Environment

1st August 1996

(**a**) S.I. 1993/2661 and 1992/2870.
(**b**) 1972 c.68.
(**c**) 1974 c.40; section 17 is prospectively repealed by Part II of Schedule 16 to the Environmental Protection Act 1990 (c.43).
(**d**) 1990 c.43; section 62 was amended by paragraph 80 of Schedule 22 to the Environment Act 1995 (c.25).
(**e**) S.I. 1996/972.

[DOE 0784]

AMENDMENT OF THE SPECIAL WASTE REGULATIONS 1996

1.   The Special Waste Regulations 1996 shall be amended as follows.

2.   In regulation 1(4) (interpretation)–

(a) in the definition of "the approved supply list"–

(i) for the words "2nd Edition" there shall be substituted the words "3rd Edition";

(ii) for the date "18th October 1994" there shall be substituted the date "24th January 1996";

(b) for the definition of "household waste" there shall be substituted the following–

""household waste" means waste which is household waste for the purposes of Part II of the 1990 Act**(a)** or which is treated as household waste for those purposes by virtue of regulation 2(1) of the Controlled Waste Regulations 1992**(b)**, other than–

(a) asbestos;

(b) waste from a laboratory;

(c) waste from a hospital, other than waste from a self-contained part of a hospital which is used wholly for the purposes of living accommodation.".

3.   For regulation 2 (meaning of special waste) there shall be substituted the following regulation–

"Meaning of special waste

2.—(1) Any controlled waste, other than household waste,–

(a) to which a six-digit code is assigned in the list set out in Part I of Schedule 2 to these Regulations (which reproduces the list of hazardous waste annexed to Council Decision 94/904/EC**(c)** establishing a list of hazardous waste pursuant to Article 1(4) of the Hazardous Waste Directive); and

(b) which displays any of the properties specified in Part II of that Schedule (which reproduces Annex III to the Hazardous Waste Directive),

is special waste.

(2) Any other controlled waste, other than household waste, which–

(a) displays the property H3-A (first indent), H4, H5, H6, H7 or H8 specified in Part II of Schedule 2 to these Regulations; or

(b) is a medicinal product, as defined in section 130 of the Medicines Act 1968**(d)** (meaning of "medicinal product" etc.), of a description, or falling within a class, specified in an order under section 58 of that Act**(e)** (medicinal products on prescription only),

is special waste.

(3) For the purposes of paragraphs (1) and (2) waste shall be treated as displaying none of the properties H4 to H8 specified in Part II of Schedule 2 to these Regulations if it satisfies none of the criteria set out in Part III of that Schedule.

(4) Part IV of Schedule 2 to these Regulations (which contains rules for the interpretation of that Schedule) shall have effect.".

4.   In regulation 4 (coding of consignments)–

(a) at the beginning of paragraph (1) there shall be inserted "Subject to paragraph (3),";

(b) after paragraph (2) there shall be added the following paragraph–

"(3) The Agency need not assign or supply a code for a consignment or round until any fee required in respect of it under regulation 14(1) has been paid."

5.   In regulation 8 (consignment notes: carrier's rounds)–

(a) in paragraph (2)(a)(ii) there shall be inserted at the beginning the words "except where the special waste to be collected on the carrier's round consists entirely of lead acid motor vehicle batteries,";

(a) *See* section 75(5) of the 1990 Act.

(b) S.I. 1992/588, amended by S.I. 1993/566, 1994/1056 and 1995/288.

(c) OJ No. L 356, 31.12.1994, p. 14.

(d) 1968 c.67; section 130 was amended by paragraph 3(7) to (10) of Schedule 1, and Schedule 2, to the Animal Health and Welfare Act 1984 (c.40).

(e) Section 58 was amended by section 1 of the Medicinal Products: Prescription by Nurses etc. Act 1992 (c.28).

(b) in paragraph (2)(b)(i) for the word "four" there shall be substituted the word "three";

(c) after paragraph (2) there shall be inserted the following paragraph–

"(2A) In a case where waste of more than one description is specified in the consignment note, either–

(a) the schedule referred to in paragraph (2)(b)(iii) shall contain a separate entry for each description of waste to be collected from each consignor showing the description of waste to which that entry relates; or

(b) each entry in the schedule shall show the different descriptions of the waste to be collected and, for each such description, the quantity of the waste to be collected.";

(d) in paragraph (4)(a), after the word "copies" there shall be inserted the words "and includes a record of the time at which it is completed";

(e) after paragraph (5) there shall be inserted the following paragraph–

"(5A) Before the removal of the last consignment of waste on the carrier's round, the carrier shall complete Part C on the three copies of the consignment note retained by him.";

(f) in paragraph (6) sub-paragraph (a) shall be omitted.

6. In regulation 14 (fees)–

(a) in paragraph (1), for the words "when it assigns or supplies", there shall be substituted "in connection with the assignment or supply of";

(b) in paragraph (2)(a), for the words "such rounds in respect of which" there shall be substituted the words "such rounds in which a single vehicle is used and in respect of which";

(c) after paragraph (2), there shall be added the following paragraph–

"(3) Where an Agency assigns or supplies a code under regulation 4(1) without the fee required under this regulation having been paid to it, the person who requested the assignment or supply shall be required to pay the fee to that Agency within the period of two months beginning with the date on which the request was made."

7. In Schedule 2 there shall be added at the end the following–

"PART IV

RULES FOR THE INTERPRETATION OF THIS SCHEDULE

1. Except in the case of a substance listed in the approved supply list, the test methods to be used for the purposes of deciding which (if any) of the properties mentioned in Part II of this Schedule are to be assigned to a substance are those described in Annex V to Council Directive 67/548/EEC(**a**), as amended by Commission Directive 92/69/EEC(**b**).

2. Any reference in Part III of this Schedule to a substance being classified as having a hazardous property, having assigned to it a particular risk phrase, or being placed within a particular category of a classification is a reference to that substance being so classified, having that risk phrase assigned to it or being placed in that category–

(i) in the case of a substance listed in the approved supply list, on the basis of Part V of that list;

(ii) in the case of any other substance, on the basis of the criteria laid down in the approved classification and labelling guide.

3. Any reference in Part III of this Schedule to the total concentration of any substances being equal to or greater than a given percentage is a reference to the proportion by weight of those substances in any waste being equal to or, as the case may be, greater than that percentage.".

(**a**) OJ No. L 196, 16.8.1967, p. 1.
(**b**) OJ No. L 383, 29.12.1992, p. 1.

EXPLANATORY NOTE

(This note is not part of the Regulations)

These Regulations amend the Special Waste Regulations 1996 (S.I. 1996/972) ("the principal Regulations"), which make provision for handling special waste and for implementing Council Directive 91/689/EEC on hazardous waste (OJ No. L.377, 31.12.1991, p. 20) ("the Directive").

Regulation 2 of and Schedule 2 to the principal Regulations define special waste. These Regulations amend that definition by–

— clarifying and updating the cross-references to the approved supply list issued for the purposes of the Chemicals (Hazard Information and Packaging for Supply) Regulations 1994; those Regulations have been amended by the Chemicals (Hazard Information and Packaging for Supply) (Amendment) Regulations 1996 (S.I. 1996/1092) and a new (3rd) edition of the approved supply list has been issued and is available from HSE Books, PO Box 1999, Sudbury, Suffolk, CO10 6FS;

— amending the definition of household waste (which is excluded from the definition of special waste).

Regulation 2 implements the definition of hazardous waste in the Directive and in particular in the list annexed to Council Decision 94/904/EC (EC OJ No. L.356, 31.12.94, p. 14). The definition extends, in accordance with Article 4 of the Directive, to certain other waste considered by the United Kingdom to display particular hazardous properties.

Regulation 4 of the principal Regulations requires the Environment Agency (in relation to England and Wales) and the Scottish Environment Protection Agency (in relation to Scotland) ("the Agencies") to give unique codes to be applied to consignments of waste. These codes are to be shown together with other required information on consignment notes which are to accompany the waste when transported. These Regulations amend regulation 4 to allow the Agencies to delay assignment of a code until payment of any fee required in respect of it. The provisions on codes do not implement any specific Community obligation.

Regulation 8 of the principal Regulations (which implements Community obligations arising under Article 5 of the Directive) makes special provision in respect of the documentation required in connection with "carrier's rounds" in which special waste is collected from a number of consignors. These Regulations amend regulation 8 to provide for only one set of documents to be required in cases where waste of more than one description is collected on a carrier's round.

Regulation 14 of the principal Regulations makes provision for the payment of fees in connection with the supply of codes under regulation 4. These Regulations provide that if a code is given before a fee is paid for it, the person who requested the code is to pay the fee within two months of that request. Regulation 14 does not implement a Community obligation.

The Regulations also make minor drafting amendments.

£5.60

Reprinted 1996 in the UK for The Stationery Office Limited under the authority and superintendence of Peter Macdonald, Controller of Her Majesty's Stationery Office and Queen's Printer of Acts of Parliament.

WO 1470   C20   10/96   1731   56219   ON 341616